HIGHLAND CATHEDRAL

THE RISE AND FALL OF THE GREAT KIRK OF ROSS

Story by Elizabeth Sutherland
Illustrations by Rachel Bevan Baker

BLACK ISLE BOOKS

Finn's story is for Iona and Rachael who asked the right questions and also for all other curious visitors, young and not so young, to our Highland Cathedral.

This book is published in celebration of the life of Ruaridh Macdonald who was born within sight of Fortrose Cathedral and within sound of Bishop Tulloch's 559-year old bell.
R.M. 1978–2018

Published by Black Isle Books
mnm982@gmail.com

First published 2019

ISBN: 978-1-5272-4250-0

Design and print management by Big Sky Print, Findhorn, Scotland

STORY TIME LINE

Rachel Bevan Baker has hidden ten little mice – Finn's friends –
among her pictures. Can you find the other ten mice?

1250
SOWING A CATHEDRAL

Failte gu! I'm Finn. I live beside St Nicolas Chapel with Brother Calum. He found me on his doorstep and he took me in. He's old now so while he prays, I plough his field, milk his cow, make our porridge, feed his chickens, cut his peats, ring his chapel bell...

I'm kept busy but I don't mind. Like I say, he's my mam and dad.

Today we had visitors. Bishop Robert from Rosemarkie and a bunch of strange men trampled through my barley field right up to the chapel door.

'Here, loon!' one of them shouted. 'Take the Bishop's horse.'

I was looking at my barley. My face was tripping me.

'What's up with you, boy?' the same fellow shouted.

Brother Calum was at my side. 'This is sacred ground,' he said, waving at the spoiled crop with a shaky hand.

'It was set aside and blessed by the monks of Rosemarkie to grow food for the poor.'

They all turned to look at my ruined barley. The Bishop laughed. He laughed! Man, was I mad.

'You'll not be needing your barley, Brother Calum,' he said. 'I've a better crop to grow.' He beckoned to me. 'Over here, boy!'

I dragged my feet, but you don't say no to a Bishop.

'Can you count?' he asked. I nod my head. Thanks to Brother Calum I can count and I can read a bit of Latin too. 'Count out 200 footsteps.'

He points me in a westerly direction and with one hand on my shoulder we count out the steps aloud, all 200 of them. Then he takes his big staff and hands it to me.

'Now plant my crook.'

So I did, pushing it hard into the barley at the far end of the field.

'What am I to grow, then?' I asked a bit cheekily, 'sticks?'

'A Cathedral, boy. We are going to grow a Cathedral. One day it will cover the whole of your field.'

'What for?' I asked, because we already have a house for God. I was still a bit fed up at losing my barley.

'To give folk a glimpse of heaven,' he said.

1297
BATTLE AND LOOT

Failte gu again! Surprised to see me? Not everyone can. One day I'll share my secret with you… Perhaps. The growing of the Cathedral is slow…slow… slow… Now, as you can see, it's almost stopped. That's because of the war against the English King Edward. All the north of Scotland belongs to him. The English are everywhere, eating our corn, stealing our cows and taking our taxes.

Last summer the big man, Lord Andrew Murray himself, rode by. 'If you want to keep your homes, join me. Fight for your families, for your country, for freedom!'

'Will we get paid?' someone shouted.

'Aye and more. English loot off the battlefield!'

Most of the quarriers, masons, carpenters, glaziers and their apprentices downed tools and joined an army to fight King Edward. There was a big battle at Stirling Bridge but with warriors like Sir Andrew and William Wallace to lead them, our side won. Great! But only a few came back with a bit of coin, true enough, and some without their arms and legs. No use here.

Even Sir Andrew died of his wounds. They buried him in Rosemarkie.

That was just one battle. The war is still on. It'll be years yet before our Cathedral is fully grown. 'To give folk a glimpse of heaven,' the Bishop said.

1350

LAD-OF-ALL-WORK
AT THE CHANONRY OF ROSS

Welcome all! Recognise me? That's right. I'm standing where my barley used to grow. The Cathedral is getting bigger, isn't it? So is the town.

In English, it's called Fortrose, but mostly it's known by its Gaelic name, *A'Chananaich*, which means the Chanonry, because of all the Canons who live in manses around the Cathedral Green. Their boss is called the Dean who lives in the Deanery. Together they are called the Chapter. They meet in the Chapter House. You can just see it hidden behind the Cathedral.

There are twenty-one Canons, all wealthy clergymen. They pay for a vicar to look after each of their parish churches all over Ross and a vicar-choral to sing in the Cathedral choir. There are nine sung services every day called the Hours, not including High Mass at the High Altar and lots of Low Masses at the little altars set round the walls.

Some local lads are choristers and they are kept busy practising or singing the services. Other lads are called acolytes and they serve the Canons at Mass. They all learn lessons from the Chanter and the sub-Chanter in the Song School up at Platcock. They are the lucky ones. Most lads and lasses are servants or fishermen or farm labourers.

Me? I'm kept busy all the time.

1380

A Crusader Calls

Failte folks! What excitement in the Chanonry today! We are having a visit from a real Crusader. Not just any Crusader. He is the bravest jouster in the land, King David's favourite knight. His name is Sir Walter Leslie the Bold and he is married to the greatest lady in Ross, the Countess Euphemia. Bishop Alexander has invited them to visit the Cathedral.

Can you see me? I am squeezed in behind the Crusader because I want to study his battle scars. Don't worry. I won't get into trouble because most people can't see me, except you. Uh-oh! Wrong there. I've been spotted by Lady Euphemia's daughter. I give her a big smile. She ducks her head and blushes, so I know she's seen me.

While the Bishop is making a long speech, I get near enough to ask her name.

'Margaret' she tells me shyly. 'What's yours?'

'Finn,' I tell her.

'Finn?' she says, 'I like that.'

Meanwhile the Bishop is asking the Crusader if he and his Lady will build a side aisle on to the Cathedral. 'All great Cathedrals are built in the form of a cross,' the Bishop is saying.

'If Elgin Cathedral can have side-aisles, if Dornoch Cathedral can also take the shape of a cross, so surely should Ross? The Cathedral Kirk of Ross is sadly lacking in aisles, Sir Walter! Lady Euphemia, will you help?'

The Crusader agrees. 'Lord Bishop,' he says, 'we have heard your request. We would have you build a chapel south of the nave and we will pay for a priest to sing Mass daily for ourselves and for the souls of our dead ancestors. You yourself will name the priest and see that he is housed and provided for in our name.'

His steward then moves forward and gifts a big bag of coins to the Canon-Treasurer while everyone else claps and praises the Lord.

1395

THE WOLF'S WIFE

Good morrow, good friends! Today the Chanonry is in mourning. Lady Euphemia is being buried in her own chapel, but not with her Crusader. Sir Walter was killed in a hunting accident long before it was finished. Lady Margaret is here with her husband, who is Lord of the Isles. She cannot see me for she is a grown woman and has lost the gift of *an Da Sealladh*, the Second Sight. She is weeping for her mother.

Poor Lady Euphemia. She had a sad ending to her life. A year after the Crusader died, she married Lord Alexander, one of King Robert II's sons, and – let me whisper it – he had a lady friend called Mariota who was his cook's daughter. Mariota gave him five sons and he brought them all to live in one of Lady Euphemia's own castles at Delny. He took all Lady Euphemia's land and money too.

I never saw him, but folk said he was a wild and wicked man. They called him the Wolf of Badenoch. What a scandal! When Euphemia complained about him to the Bishops of Moray and Ross, they summoned him to court to make him support her. He was so angry that he and his thugs set fire to Elgin, both the town and the Cathedral. He was excommunicated, which means no friends, no feasting, no hunting and no church. The Pope himself gave Lady Euphemia a divorce. She never got over the shame.

But her south aisle is a splendid memorial, is it not?

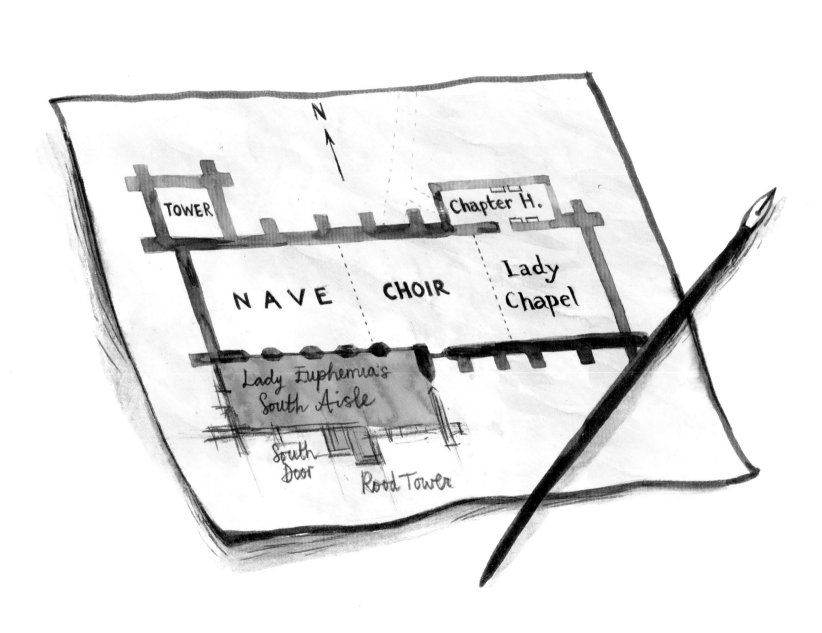

1417
BEWARE – PLAGUE!

The Black Death is back among us. How and why it comes no one knows for sure. Some folk suspect the chandler, John Vass, for he was the first to sicken and within two days he was dead. It is said that he received a box of clothing from his son who had died in foreign parts. Seemingly the plague was hiding in the box and jumped out and caught him the instant he opened it.

Most of the Canons have fled for no one is safe these days, but my friend, old Archdeacon William of Kiltearn, remains. He has gathered together the only men brave enough to do his bidding, his vicar-choral (who has to do as he is told), old Dod who is crazy and me. He has told the gravedigger to prepare a deep hole by the sundial close to his own manse. He has given his vicar a censer filled with frankincense, the best he can find.

Old Dod and I both have bells and the Archdeacon carries a Bible. He has taken a white linen sheet from his own bed and we have all been to the house of Mistress Macdonald, an old dame who was dying of the plague. He laid the sheet across her dying body and prayed in Latin for her living soul. The vicar swung the censer till the incense rose in dense white clouds. Dod and I rang our bells mightily (my favourite task!).

The moment her spirit departed, Archdeacon William picked up the four corners of the sheet, knotted them together and caught the evil plague. He carried it carefully to the grave. The whole town turned out to watch the burial, but at a safe distance for everyone was dead afraid.

So far there has only been one new victim, a sturdy chorister, and, *Deo gratias*, he has recovered!

No one will go near the grave for folk are still frightened. They call it the Holeridge. Archdeacon William says that is just their ignorance, for *horlogium* means sundial in Latin, which all the canons speak.

1455
A Peep at Heaven

Greetings, good folk! Today the whole of the Chanonry is gathered in our great Cathedral. A letter has come from King James II to Bishop Thomas de Tulloch proclaiming that the Chanonry has been granted a Royal Charter to become a Free Burgh. This is great news for it means that folk can buy and sell, import and export goods without interference from anyone. Burgesses are free men once they have paid their annual tax to the king himself. The Chanonry is now called 'The Royal Burgh of Fortrose and Rosemarkie'.

So what do you think? Now that the Cathedral is finished, does it give you a wee glimpse of heaven?

When the Bishop, the Dean and the Canons are dressed up in their splendid robes, when the gold and silver Communion vessels on the High Altar and the side altars glitter in the light of a hundred candles, when the sweet smoke from the incense turns the rafters misty, when the choir sing psalms, then, yes, it reminds me a wee bit of heaven.

Heaven is a lot warmer though! In winter, the Cathedral can be mighty cold.

1500
MARKET DAY

Welcome all! Today is June 5th – St Boniface Day. Fortrose has a big market on his name day and all the Canons and choristers take a holiday. The Canons like to practise archery on the Cathedral Green, or play at bowls and walk their dogs. The boys play football and sometimes I join in. The girls dress themselves – and their dolls – in their best gowns and everybody spends a lot of money!

Can you see me? Sometimes I play with the Dean's dog. He's called Prince and he can see me. Most animals can.

Oh, sorry, I should have told you! The Cathedral is dedicated to St Peter and St Boniface. Our Boniface is a Latin nickname which means 'do-gooder'. His real name was Curadan. Curadan-Boniface was the Pictish monk who built a church dedicated to St Peter in Rosemarkie 800 years ago. St Peter was a fisherman, a friend of Jesus and the first Bishop of Rome.

1504

THE PILGRIM KING

The King is here! We all love Jamie IV. He is handsome and kind and just. He loves us Highlanders so much that he stops by most years on Pilgrimage to the shrine of St Duthac in Tain. Sometimes he brings his Queen, wee Maggie Tudor. She is sister to the English King Henry VIII.

Today he is alone on his Arab steed. They are saying he has ridden from Stirling – over a hundred miles – in two days!

They also say he wears an iron chain under his clothing to which he adds a new link every year in sorrow for his sins.

We lads are the first to greet him by the Cross on the Ness. We hold his wondrous horse while he kneels to pray. He greets the Bishop and the Canons in Latin, speaks Scots and French to his court and Gaelic to us lads.

He plays the 30-string clarsach, he laughs a lot and he loves dancing. He is generous too. He gave five pounds to the Canons for feasting and threw us lads a handful of groats.

1560

THE BEGINNING OF THE END

You won't believe what has just happened! Don Paterson, the shoemaker and his wife Elspeth came into the cathedral. They tried to remove one of the side altars. His mother-in-law, Goodie Hossack, took the candlesticks, and their daughter Joan the picture of the Holy Family. Dean Moneypenny was sent for. 'You'll not be needing them any more,' grumbled Don as the Dean made him return them.

In a way Don is right. Parliament has just passed a law forbidding any priest to say Mass, pray to the saints or obey the Pope. 'Don and his like will be back,' sighed one of the Canons gloomily. 'This is beginning of the end.'

I hear the whispers. They are getting louder and louder.

'*What does God want with pictures and silver candlesticks and rich clothing?*

'*Why do we have to speak to God or read the Bible in Latin? Does He not understand the good Scots tongue?*'

'*We have voices and hearts and brains. Surely God prefers prayers that come from the heart, not gabbled from a book.*'

'*The chanting of priests, the burning of incense and the reverence of dead bones are for heathens! We are God's people.*'

Finally Parliament has listened. The old ways are gone forever. What will happen to my beautiful Cathedral now?

1562
Long Live the Queen!

Today Queen Mary, the one we call Queen of Scots, rode to Fortrose! The whole town came out to see her and most of them cheered. I'm sorry to say some boo-ed and you could hear the word 'Papist!' hissed at her, but not too loudly for she had her soldiers with her. I hope she didn't hear, for she is beautiful and kind.

Our Bishop, Henry Sinclair, is her friend. She has been staying with him in his Palace. Some say he has broken the law and celebrated Mass with her in his private oratory. Poor Queen Mary! Her soldiers had to fight to get back her castle in Inverness which was occupied by Alexander Gordon. His captain barred the door in her face.

Her soldiers caught him and stuck his head up over his own gate.

She rode up to the Cathedral and ignored the Louping-on Stane placed there to help riders mount.

The Choir sang for her most beautifully, but there was no Mass since Parliament has banned it.

The thieving continues. Townsfolk help themselves to candlesticks and pictures. A few men broke into the Treasury in the Chapter House one night and stole the gold and silver vessels. Some of the Canons are no better. I have seen them help themselves to anything of value: candles, wine, vestments and fine linen.

Where will it all end?

1572
FROM BAD TO WORSE

The thieving has not stopped. See the ladders all round the cathedral walls? Can you guess what the men are doing? Word has come from the King James VI's Treasurer, Lord Ruthven in Edinburgh, to take all the lead from the roof because he says, 'the cathedral is no parish kirk but a monastery to sustain idle bellies.'

He is very ignorant, for our Cathedral was never a monastery. The Canons were never monks.

When Master George Munro, the old Canon-Chancellor, protested that the roof would leak, he was told to get it thatched. Some townsfolk are shocked to see such destruction and some are broken-hearted. Very few are celebrating.

1579

THIEVES AND
CLAN MACKENZIE

Worse. Clan Mackenzie has invaded the town – 3000 of them. See where they are living? In the Cathedral Steeple and the Canons' manses. Look where they stable their horses. In the Green among the gravestones.

When Bishop Hepburn died, the Chief, Colin Cam, turned his family out and occupied the palace. They steal from the townsfolk, bully the burgesses, frighten the women and bury their dead in the south aisle.

Because no one can control the Mackenzies, King Jamie Saxt has now put them in charge of law and order!

1626
A University in the Highlands

Good news at last! Bishop Lindsay has received a letter from King Charles I himself. He read it out from the pulpit after Morning Prayer. You should have seen the smiles all round because even though it's cold and leaky, most Fortrose folk still love their Cathedral.

This is what the King wrote: '*For removing of ignorance and barbarity from the northern parts of our kingdom a college be erected at the Chanonry of Ross, and to let the King know what the cost of building and the employment of masters, professors and poor students will amount to yearly so we may give a helping hand.*'

Isn't that wonderful? The Town Council have already begun to build a new Clock Tower to house our special bell gifted by Bishop Tulloch away back in 1460. It's a good start.

1638

REVOLT IN FORTROSE

We were all so hopeful, but it hasn't lasted.

People blame King Charles I. He ordered every church in Scotland to use a proper prayer book. Our Bishop Maxwell helped to produce a Scottish edition of the English *Book of Common Prayer*. No one in Edinburgh wanted it. No one in Fortrose wants it either.

Early this morning some schoolboys crept into our Cathedral. They seized the big book from the pulpit and ran away with it down to the Ness Cross now called the Witch's Stone.

One of them started a fire to burn the book but it began to rain which put the fire out, so they ran down to the beach, tore the book to pieces and threw them out to sea. Yes, truly, they did, because I was there!

Bishop Maxwell was so upset that he caught the next ferry south and he has never come back.

1638
BANISHED BISHOPS

What a terrible year. Winter is coming and cold news with it.

The **National Covenant** has come to the Cathedral. After the morning service, everyone lined up to sign it. Not everyone wanted to but most townsfolk did. Some wrote in their own blood.

They have promised to follow the new Reformed Religion and to reject the old Roman Catholic beliefs. They are now called **Covenanters**. They wear dark clothes They try hard to be righteous and to make everyone else behave, but they have forgotten how to laugh and have fun. Some of them are so fierce they frighten me.

Bishop Maxwell and fourteen other Scottish Bishops were denounced and deposed at the General Assembly of the Church in Glasgow. They said our Bishop played cards and diced and drank wine and wore robes and travelled on Sunday.

All true, but he also preached powerfully, prayed to God, loved his neighbours and visited the sick. So why was he condemned? Because the King believes that he is the Head of the Church by Divine Right and rules through his Bishops, while Covenanters believe that God alone is head of the Church and head of the King too, so there is no need for Bishops. Everybody is arguing with each other.

1639

CIVIL WAR

Twelve months of misery have led to this: Covenanters have raised an army to fight against King Charles and his soldiers so now there is civil war. Scot against Scot, Highlander against Lowlander, English against Scots, neighbour against neighbour.

Here in the Chanonry most people signed the new **National League and Covenant** but some slipped away to fight for King Charles. The battles were fierce all over the country, even here in the Highlands. Then the King himself was beheaded in London. Most people were deeply shocked and ashamed because the Scottish people had sold him to the English for £200,000. Some say, like Judas, they betrayed their king for money.

Fortrose is now occupied by English soldiers. One of their jobs is to demolish the Castle and the Bishop's Palace. They are taking away every single stone to build a prison in Inverness called the Citadel. Our high-heid-yin, Big Kenny Mackenzie, Provost of Fortrose Town Council, and the third Earl of Seaforth has been captured and imprisoned there by the English Puritan soldiers.

Everyone is poor. Trade is dead. The taxes are higher than ever to pay for the army. Lord Oliver Cromwell who rules us all from London is saying, 'Scotland is a very ruined nation.'

Now that there is war, people are poorer and the Kirk rules stricter. Master Munro, the minister, tells us we had better behave ourselves or we will all go to hell. He even makes me shake in my boots.

There is a special seat in the cathedral called the Stool of Repentance. The naughty people have to sit there and confess their sins in front of the congregation. If anyone misses church and is found bowling, playing at cards or quoits or working on the Sabbath day, he can be fined up to eight pounds Scots.

There are big fines too if you don't remove your muck and midden from the streets within two days. Woe to any woman who washes her clothes in the springs or burns. They are now ordered to carry the water to their own back yards to keep the town clean. No chance!

1660
A New King

We have a King again! Charles II is a Stuart, he is a Scot and he is welcome. He was crowned in Scone in 1651 and everybody is happy and hopeful.

King Charles summoned his first Parliament in Edinburgh and cancelled all the old Acts, even the **National Covenant**. The King is head of the church once more.

We are to have a Scottish Episcopalian Bishop too, David Lindsay, not that we will see much of him because he has gone to England with the King.

Big Kenny, Chief of Clan Mackenzie, is free again. He has started to build himself a grand new home in Fortrose called Seaforth House. He and his wife, Lady Isabella (rather nippy) and their children are living there while their castle at Brahan is being restored.

I helped to build it.

1661
FIRE!

God bless us all! The townsfolk have been complaining to Provost Big Kenny Mackenzie that the pigeons that roost in the Cathedral thatch are eating their crops. Big Kenny took his gun to shoot them. It was a windy morning.

A spark from the gun was all that was needed! The old cathedral thatch caught fire and the wind carried the great flames to other roofs. Soon the whole town was alight. Folk formed a chain to the wells. (Can you see me?) Others brought ladders. But by evening the Cathedral had no thatch and half the houses were burned. No one got hurt though, except of course for my poor Cathedral.

1670

AN UNWISE SEER

I wish I had not seen what happened next, but I did. I always liked *Coinneach Odhar*, Brown Kenneth. Folk call him the Brahan Seer. He was one of the few people who could always see me.

He spoke of strange things yet to come, like carriages without horses on the roads and horrid black rain falling on the hills.

He should have known better than to anger Countess Isabella, especially with her husband away in Paris. *Coinneach* said Big Kenny was carrying on with a French lady – true, but he was a fool to tell her – just asking for trouble. Lady Isabella had him arrested and brought to the Cathedral for trial as a witch. When he was condemned to be burned to death in a spiked tar barrel on Chanonry Point, he took out his magic stone which had a hole in it, lifted it to his eye and uttered what people now call the 'Doom of the Mackenzies'.

I see into the far future. I see a chief, the last of his house, both deaf and dumb. He will be father of four fine sons, all of whom will die before him...

After lamenting the last and most promising of his sons, he himself will sink into the grave. His possessions shall be inherited by a white-hooded widow from the East and she is to kill her sister.

I can't see all that happening anytime soon, can you?

1689

'THE GLORIOUS REVOLUTION'

What's so 'Glorious' about it? Our Cathedral is crumbling to bits. Townsfolk steal the stones to build new houses for themselves.

The old Covenanters refuse to accept the Bishops. They have left their churches and attend services in the open air called Conventicles. These are strictly against the law but no one cares.

Bishop Ramsay has accepted the estimate provided by the mason, George Ross, for basic repairs to the Cathedral. £2,665! All agree that the building is dangerous but still nothing is done.

Since King Charles II died in 1685 politics are in a real mess.

The Scottish Parliament met in Edinburgh to decide who should be king. Some were Protestant William and Mary-ites (William is the Dutch husband of Charles' daughter Mary) and some were James-ites. (James is Charles' brother.) Most call the James-ites 'Jacobites', from the Latin *Jacobus* for James.

The William and Mary-ites won. James ran away to France. Bishops have been abolished again! All because the Bishop of Edinburgh swore loyalty to James. Now Fortrose has no minister and no money to pay for one, or for repairs to the Cathedral.

1696

UNFIT FOR PURPOSE

Fortrose Town Council has sent this petition to the Scots Parliament pleading for help.

Since abolishing Episcopacy [Bishops] our cathedral is still vacant and there are no other funds for the maintenance of the parson for all the rents of the Bishopric now belong to His Majesty's tax collectors. The congregation are sheep almost lost and going astray for want of a shepherd and likewise the Church [Cathedral] is so ruined and demolished that they dare not enter it. Some parts of these rents must be allowed for repairing it.

King William and Queen Mary disagree so no help there. People go to worship in Rosemarkie Church, but the minister there, Master David Angus, has just been sacked because he is an Episcopalian!

Presbyterian ministers are hard to please. Master Robert Findlay is particularly unpopular for he scolds his congregation for the meanness of his stipend and the lack of a manse to live in. The Town Council protests that he gives strangers a bad impression. The congregation complains that the Cathedral is too dangerous so now there are no services held there at all.

1700
CATHEDRAL PRISONERS

Our Chapter House is now called the Tolbooth. It badly needs repair. The Town Council use the upper room for meetings during the week and the congregation use it on Sunday for services – take your own stool – while the lower room, or undercroft, is the town prison.

They are asking local merchants and Dingwall and Inverness Burghs for 200 merks for a new roof. The Town Clerk has contributed just 40 shillings!

1707

GREAT BRITAIN IS BORN

So today we have become one with England.

Our new Queen Anne says that for *'security and happiness of England and Scotland'* our Parliaments should be united. We can keep our own law and law courts but we will share our pounds and pennies and there will be one flag.

I hope that something may now be done to repair our Cathedral, but fear the worst. How can money be spent on manses or cathedral repairs when the poverty of the people is so pitiful?

Happiness promised by Queen Anne still seems a long way off.

1716 AND AFTERWARDS
'A PROPER MIDDEN'

Our Provost, The Earl of Seaforth, is in jail because he supports the Jacobites who drink the health of James, the Old Pretender King across the water.

Church of Scotland members argue with Episcopalians because they won't pray for the new King, brought over from Hanover in Germany, called George.

Once again everyone is quarrelling. Jacobites against Hanoverians, Highlanders against Lowlanders, Scots against English.

It all came to a head at the Battle of Sheriffmuir, where the Jacobites were beaten.

As for the Cathedral Green, just look at it!

Weeds grow among the ruins. Dung hills stink outside every house, rubbish piles high on the Green, cows browse between the fallen stones and pigs root freely among the graves. It would break your heart.

1723

A Big Tidy-up

At last the Town Council has ordered the Chapter House to be made fit for public worship. The remaining stones are being removed from the Cathedral ruins for the construction of a proper High Street.

I have made a new friend!

He is the young Episcopalian minister called Lewis Grant. Sometimes he can see me so I do odd jobs for him. He is not allowed to have a church so he holds services in his home, which is called a meeting-house.

If he refuses to pray for the Hanoverian King George he can either go to prison or be transported to a distant country for life.

Only five Episcopalian families may worship together at the same time in his house.

Episcopalians are thought to side with the Jacobites. They are called 'non-jurants'. The government is trying to stamp out the Jacobites and the Episcopalians altogether.

Good luck with that!

1746
CHARLIE'S YEAR

We could hear the cannons roar across the Firth at the big Battle of Culloden. It was a terrible fight and the Jacobites lost. All those suspected of supporting the Old Pretender's son, Bonnie Prince Charlie, have been arrested.

The Tolbooth prison is full. Butcher Cumberland, King George's son, who won the battle, is ruthless. Clansmen, Episcopalian and Roman Catholic priests are forced to skulk in the heather. No one is safe.

I warned my friend, Master Lewis Grant, the Episcopalian minister, that he was in danger.

He escaped out the back door while some Fortrose folk broke through the front. The mob was about to set his house on fire. 'No, no, no!' his neighbours shrieked. 'Our houses will burn too!' So they removed his roof and burned it on the Cathedral Green.

Master Grant caught the ferry across the Firth and has sailed for London, or so I heard. Meanwhile in Fortrose, the Town Council has sacked the schoolmaster. He was teaching the boys to say, 'Long live Bonnie Prince Charlie!'

1762

A NEW BISHOP FOR ROSS

Hello, everyone! I'm still here.

Master Grant is back again taking services in his house. He's getting on a bit at 80 but he can still read without spectacles and he can still walk to Cromarty to take services there.

You won't believe it but there's a new Episcopalian Bishop of Ross! He's called Robert Forbes and he is a minister from Leith. Bishop Robert is a jolly man and brave too, because he is still a Jacobite.

He is delighted to find a warm welcome everywhere he goes because no-one much minds about Episcopalians since the Jacobites were beaten at Culloden.

He and his wife came all the way up from Edinburgh to Inverness by chaise. Master Grant met him off the ferry at Chanonry Point and took him to see his Cathedral. They climbed up the bell tower and on to the roof of the south aisle. He remarked on the grass growing on the thatch. It's long enough to mow!

I took his baggage to Kenneth Mathieson's tavern and he entertained seven to dinner that night. He was mightily pleased with the meal. Kenny gave him eight meat dishes, fruit and the best claret and stabled his horses. All for one pound, fifteen shillings and four pence with tips included. Mr Grant told the Bishop that Kenny imported his claret himself to avoid paying tax. Maybe that would explain the deep, dark cellars hereabouts?

Next day he held a service of Morning Prayer in Mr Grant's meeting-house and afterwards preached a sermon and confirmed twenty-nine children and adults. Two of them are little black boys called Charlie Corker and John Forbes from the plantations in Jamaica. They are great favourites in the town.

1797
SACRILEGE!

Hail, friends! Today I am sad and mad. Some workmen who were supposed to mend a window in the Tolbooth decided instead to break open one of the table tombs in Lady Euphemia's chapel in search of treasure.

They had no idea of who was buried there, nor did they care. All they wanted was gold. I know that Bishop Robert Cairncross lies there and that he was buried over 250 years ago in 1545, because I was there.

He was a good man, a monk who had become the Abbot of Holyrood, and Lord Treasurer of Scotland in 1528.

The robbers came by night after the curfew bell and forced open the stone coffin. They found the inside plastered white. His body was intact and he was wearing a beautiful cope embroidered with gold crosses, and white silk gloves and stockings. They also found his crozier cunningly carved and made of gilded oak.

But there was no treasure. They handled him so roughly that his body crumbled away to dust, but what did they care. Master Wood, parish Minister of Rosemarkie, preserved what he could of the clothing and the crozier. Today you may see them for yourself at the National Museum in Edinburgh.

1815
'I SEE INTO THE FAR FUTURE...'

Here I am again.

Blizzards prevented many from attending the Chief of Clan Mackenzie's funeral. All the black clothes turned white as Francis Humberstone Mackenzie of Brahan, Lord Seaforth, Baron of Kintail, was laid to rest in the west end of the south aisle.

All the whispers I heard in the Cathedral today were about the fulfilment of *Coinneach Odhar*'s prophecy. The Highlands are full of stories about second sight. Many have been thought up after the event. Not this one though. Remember?

I see into the far future. I see a chief, the last of his house, both deaf and dumb. He will be father of four fine sons, all of whom will die before him...

After lamenting the last and most promising of his sons, he himself will sink into the grave. His possessions shall be inherited by a white-hooded widow from the East and she is to kill her sister.

It has all come true. Francis became deaf and dumb from scarlet fever caught as a child. He had ten children, four of whom were sons who all died before him. You can read their names too on the white stone tablet in the south aisle. His daughter, Mary, his heiress, came home from India wearing the white cap of a widow. As a woman, she could inherit his castle at Brahan, but she could not become chief of the clan. Clan Mackenzie was to be without a chief – *Caberfeidh* as they call him – for 150 years. And Mary was at the reins of the pony carriage which overturned and killed her sister Caroline.

64

I remember when Lady Isabella taunted my good friend *Coinneach Odhar* all those years ago that he would soon be in hell, the Seer made one last prophecy:

After my death two birds,
a raven and a dove,
will circle my ashes.
If the raven alight first
then you have told the truth,
but if it be the dove, then my
hopes are well-founded.

The crowd on Chanonry Point waited and watched. Both birds circled the ashes but it was the dove that alighted while the raven flew away. So I was told. So it is said.

You'll find the Seer's memorial stone on the very tip of Chanonry Point. If you've a mind to see it, spare a thought for poor *Coinneach Odhar*, burned to death in the ferry-beacon barrel of tar.

1828
WHAT HAPPENED NEXT?

Hello there!

Now that the Cathedral has become a ruin, no one wants to take care of it. Local folk continue to be buried in the Green; the Town Council and the Court still meet in the upper Chapter House while prisoners stay locked up below.

The townsfolk are building fine new churches for themselves. Most folk no longer have the money, interest or time to worry about the Cathedral.

But some people still care. Robert Ross, head of the newly formed Scottish Office of Works has himself inspected the ruins and reported that at least £100 is needed to preserve them.

1848 AND ONWARDS
A FUTURE SECURED

The Cathedral is now Crown property. A strong wall has been built round what is left of the Green and yew trees planted for protection.

Another twenty years go by...

The site of the old nave and bell-tower are being dug out by archaeologists and laid out in gravel. I am sure one of them can see me.

Today *Historic Environment Scotland* looks after what is left of my Cathedral – the South Aisle, the Chapter House, the spacious Green and its sentinel yew trees – with more care than I could ever give. I am free at last.

From time to time, though, I like to come back. I cried when the British Legion built the Memorial Gateway with the names of those killed in the First and Second World Wars. I remember so many wars, too many deaths.

I was there for the great celebrations of 1955 when the Royal Burgh celebrated its Quincentenary.

Every August on the second Thursday, when once again the Green comes alive with music and laughter at the re-enactment of St Boniface Fair, there I am.

I am there without fail on Christmas Eve when the carol singers remind me of the long-gone choristers.

Perhaps some of you may see me. If you do, be sure to say **hello**.

Yesterday and Today and Tomorrow...

So who am I?

A long time ago, so the story goes, the Little People lived in Rosemarkie Fairy Glen. The great wizard Michael Scot commanded them to build two cathedrals, one in Fortrose and one in Elgin. The Little People work hard but sometimes they get things spectacularly wrong. Elgin Cathedral turned up in Fortrose, and Fortrose in Elgin! Perhaps I am one of those Little People whose punishment was to stay here forever?

No?

In that case, remember Brother Calum? I told you he found me on his doorstep. Maybe, though, I found him. Brother Calum was old and ill and struggling. My Master decided he needed help so I was sent. When he died, maybe my Master decided to make me Guardian of the new Cathedral?

You have a Guardian Angel too, don't you?

No?

Well, perhaps it happened this way. When Brother Calum died I got a job in Arkendeith quarrying stones for the masons. It was heavy work and dangerous. One day a stone fell on my head and that was the end of me. Or was it? Did Bishop Robert bury me under the corner-stone of the new Cathedral and command my soul to watch over it for ever?

So perhaps I'm a ghost. Or maybe I'm none of these.

Perhaps I'm just a story a granny told her grandchildren.

But remember this. There are more things in the multiverse than you can ever know. **I may even be one of them.**

Glossary

acolyte: a person assisting a priest at a religious service.

aisle: passage between rows of seats; a side division of a church separated by pillars from the nave.

barley: a cereal used for bread, brewing ale and feeding farm animals.

Bishop: a senior clergyman in charge of a diocese with the power to make new priests.

Canons: the cathedral clergymen known collectively as 'the Chapter'.

cathedral: the principal church of a diocese.

catholic: universal: relating to the historic doctrine of Western Christianity. Catholic, Roman: relating to a major branch of the Catholic Church ruled by the Pope in Rome.

censer: an ornate container for burning incense (resin) in church. Incense creates a sweet smelling smoke intended to carry prayers up to heaven. The censer is swung briskly by a thurifer to keep the fire alive.

chaise: horse-drawn carriage for one or two people usually with open top and two wheels.

chandler: a shop keeper who made and sold candles and other hardware.

chantry: a chapel endowed for the celebration of masses for the donor's soul.

Chapter House: a building used for housing cathedral robes and treasure and for meetings of the Cathedral canons.

chorister: choir-boy.

Confirm and Confirmation: the bishop lays his hands on the candidate who then becomes a full member (Communicant) of the Church.

cope: a long loose cloak worn by a priest or a bishop on special occasions.

crook: a shepherd's stick with a curved end also used by bishops.

crozier: another name for a bishop's crook.

Crusades: journeys made by Christians from all over Europe to recover by force the Holy Land from the Muslims.

Crusader: literally means 'signed by the Cross'. Any person who fought for the Holy Land.

Dean: principal priest of a cathedral.

Deo Gratias: Latin for 'Thank God'.

diocese: a portion of land divided into parishes, such as Ross-shire, under the care of a bishop.

Episcopal: relating to a church governed by or having bishops.

excommunicate: officially forbid a person the Christian sacraments.

Failte gu: 'welcome' in Gaelic.

glazier: person who fits glass into windows or doors.

groat: silver coin worth 4 old pence. Originally a cowrie shell.

Louping-on Stane: a large stone purposefully placed to help riders mount a horse.

Mass: the main Christian service in Catholic churches; also called High Mass, Eucharist (Thanksgiving in Greek) or Holy Communion.

merk: a silver coin worth about 14 pence.

monk: member of a religious community who has taken vows of poverty, chastity and obedience. He lives in a monastery.

nave: central part of a church building.

non-jurant: person who refused to swear loyalty to the Hanoverian monarchy.

oratory: a small chapel or room consecrated for private services or prayer.

Papist: derogatory term for a Roman Catholic.

pilgrim: a person who journeys (goes on pilgrimage) to a sacred place for religious reasons.

Parson: a priest, vicar or minister.

plague: a highly infectious, usually fatal, epidemic disease.

Presbyterian: relating to a Protestant church governed by ministers of equal rank: the established Church of Scotland.

Protestant: member of a Christian church separated from Roman Catholicism at the Reformation.

Provost: Senior Officer of a school, university, Scottish town council or post-Reformation cathedral.

quarrier: person who cuts stone from deep pits called quarries.

Reformation: 16th century movement for the reform of the Roman Catholic church ending in the establishment of the Protestant churches.

Royal Charter: a written grant or permission from the monarch.

sacrilege: misuse of something regarded as holy.

skulk: to hide (also to scowl).

steward: a person paid to look after the property and welfare of others.

Tolbooth: town-hall containing town jail.

Vicar: a clergyman in charge of a parish.

Vicar-choral: an adult singer employed by a canon to take his place in the cathedral choir.

ACKNOWLEDGEMENTS

Special thanks, appreciation and love to Vee Walker for her advice, encouragement and practical help with my manuscript: Mike, Jerry and Ali and their families without whom this story would never have been conceived, written and brought to publication: Rachel Bevan Baker for bringing Finn's story to life with her humorous and skilful illustrations: Sylvia Macdonald for her amazing kindness and generosity: the Very Rev'd Gerald Stranraer-Mull for his historical and theological advice: Fortrose and Rosemarkie Community Council for their interest and banking facilities: to Anna-Kristina Larsson at Big Sky Print for her presentation, advice and patience: finally to all those of you who have so generously supported the publication of Highland Cathedral. Rachel and I couldn't have done any of it without you. Thank you.

Elizabeth Sutherland

THE SUPPORTERS OF HIGHLAND CATHEDRAL
OR THOSE THEY WISHED TO REMEMBER

Alister & Lesley Clunas

Allan Cameron

Allan Thomson

Alison Garraway

Alison Brough

Anne Balfour

Anonymous

Anthony & Jane Bryant

Arthur Mather

Ben & Angela Callanan

Bill & Brenda Martin

Bill & Terry Fraser

Bridget Houston

Barbara Broadbent

Carola Martin-Smith

Catriona Munro

Clare & Mark Hemsworth

Colonel AA Fairrie

David Hart

Davine Sutherland

Debbie Cameron

Des Heath

Diana Hamilton-Jones

Elizabeth Marshall

Eve Harris

Florence (Kate) Cutler

Fortrose Brownies

Fran Tilbrook

Gerald & Jenny Thornton

Helen Robinson, Rosemarkie

Helen Robinson, Singapore

IAC & EMW Brown

Dr I & Mrs S Basham

Ione Tayler

Isobel Anderson & Michael Taylor

Jane Verburg

JE McQueen

Joan MacInnes

Professor John & Mrs Joyce Watson

John G Muir

Joyce Stevenson

Jubilate Choir Fortrose

Julian & Charlotte Callanan

June & Benny Elrick

Jurgen & Carol Diethe

Karen & Mike Plested

Kathleen Armstrong

Kathy Fraser

Katie, Ryan & Finn Staudte

Kathryn Brain

Lady Joanna Young

Laura & Jerry Marshall

Louise & Hayden Jeffery

Lucca & Freddie Johnstone

Maggie Wynton

Mairi Mae Young

Margaret Ewart

Marian McKenzie Johnston

Maureen & Mike Marshall

Father Mel Langille

Pam & David Macintyre

Peter Furniss

Rachel Brown of Fortrose Bay
Campsite

Roy & Katie Nelson

Sarah Bevan-Baker

Simon & Lisa Cutler

Spar Shop customers, Rosemarkie

Steven & Jane Scott

Susan Plowman at Studio Jewellery
Workshop, Fortrose

Susie Mullen

Sylvia Macdonald

Tulloch Homes Ltd

Vee Walker

ABOUT THE AUTHOR

Elizabeth Sutherland was born in Fife, home-schooled in Dundee then educated at St Leonards School in St Andrews and the University of Edinburgh where she obtained a Certificate in Social Science. She married the Rev'd John D. Marshall in 1946 and has three children, five grandchildren and fourteen great-grandchildren. She was Social Worker for the Scottish Episcopal Church from 1974-81 and honorary Curator of Groam House Museum in Rosemarkie from 1982-93. Author of numerous articles, short stories, children's books, novels and non-fiction books she has a special interest in local history. Half a Fifer and half an Orcadian, she likes to call herself a Pict.

ABOUT THE ARTIST

Born and brought up in the Black Isle, Rachel Bevan Baker is an illustrator and animator who has always enjoyed telling stories in a visual form. After studying illustration in Glasgow School of Art she completed an MA in Animation at the Royal College of Art, graduating in 1995. She then founded Red Kite Animations with producer Ken Anderson and directed award-winning films for C4, S4C and BBC Alba. Rachel now balances teaching Art & Design in schools with producing her own work inspired by local stories, memories and nature.